FOR OLIVER

Text and illustrations © 1971, 2005 Anne and Harlow Rockwell
This edition first published in the UK 2005 by Mathew Price Limited
The Old Glove Factory, Bristol Road, Sherborne, Dorset DT9 4HP
Designed by Douglas Martin
The right of Anne and Harlow Rockwell to be identified as
authors of this work has been asserted by them in accordance with
the Copyright, Designs and Patents Act, 1988
Printed in China
ISBN 1-84248-163-0

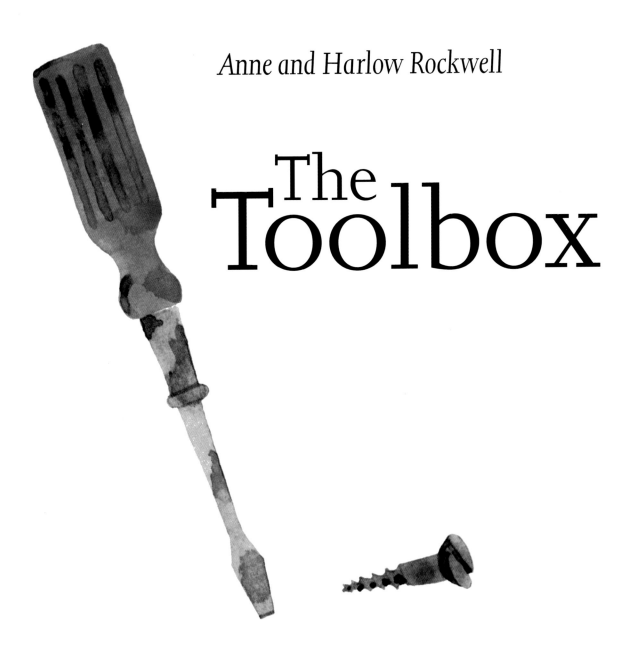

Anne and Harlow Rockwell

The Toolbox

Mathew Price Limited

In my cellar there is a toolbox.
It is dark brown where hands
have touched it.

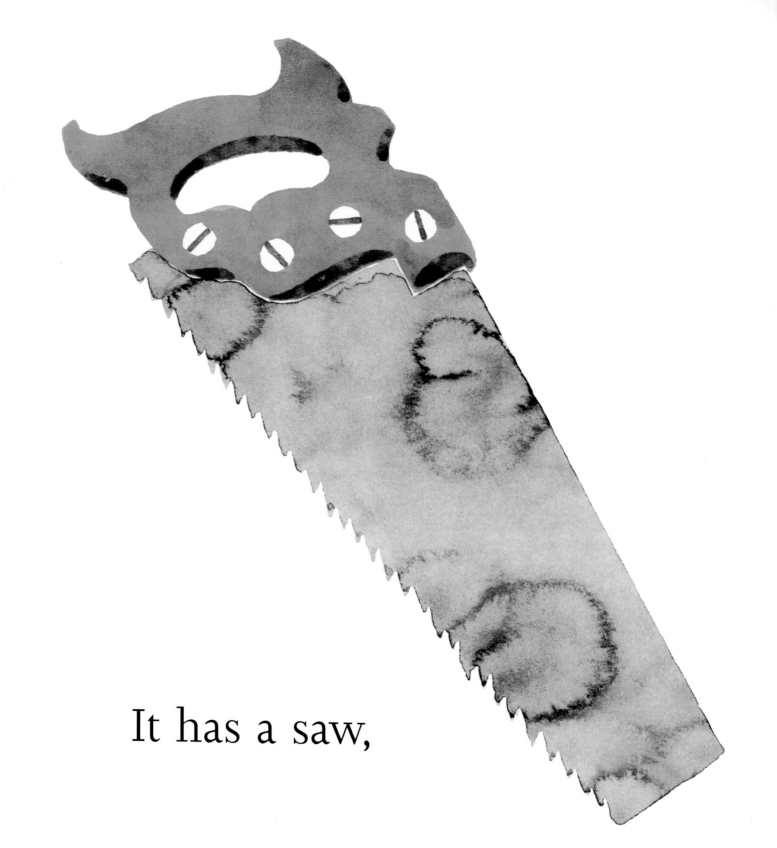

It has a saw,

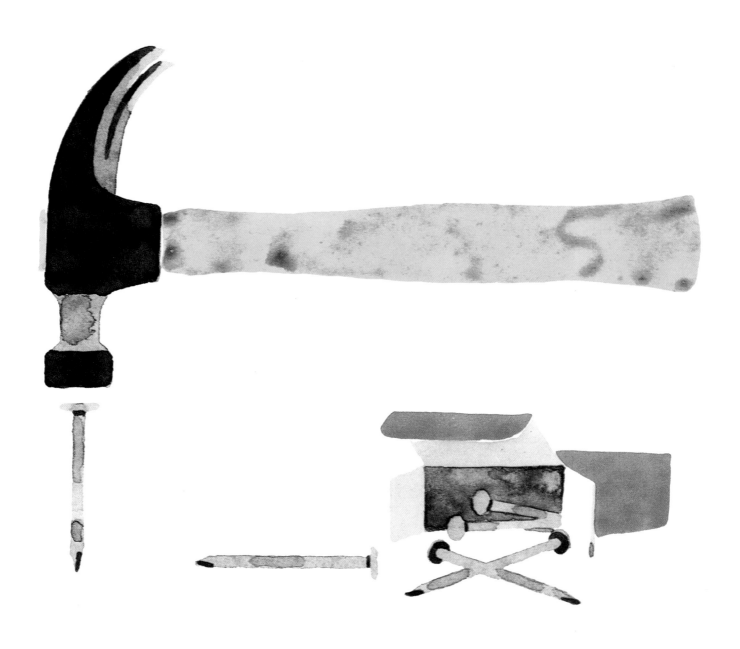

and a hammer and nails,

and a drill that
goes round and
round

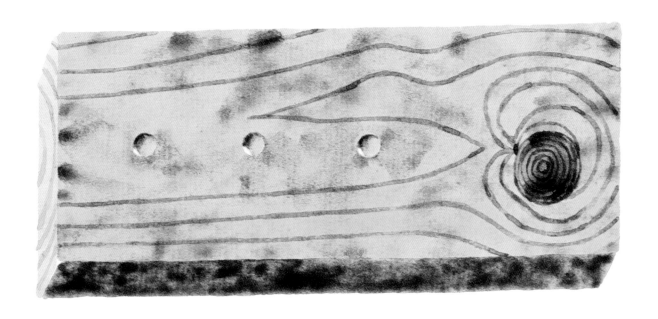

and makes holes in wood.

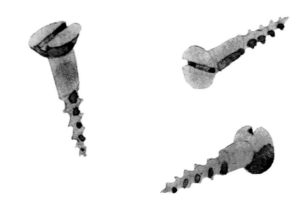

It has screws and a screwdriver

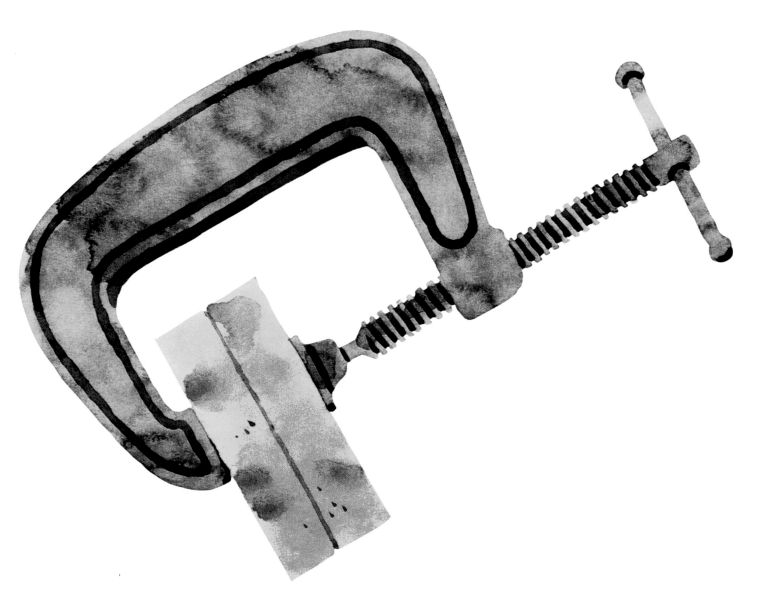

and there is a clamp that holds
pieces of wood together.

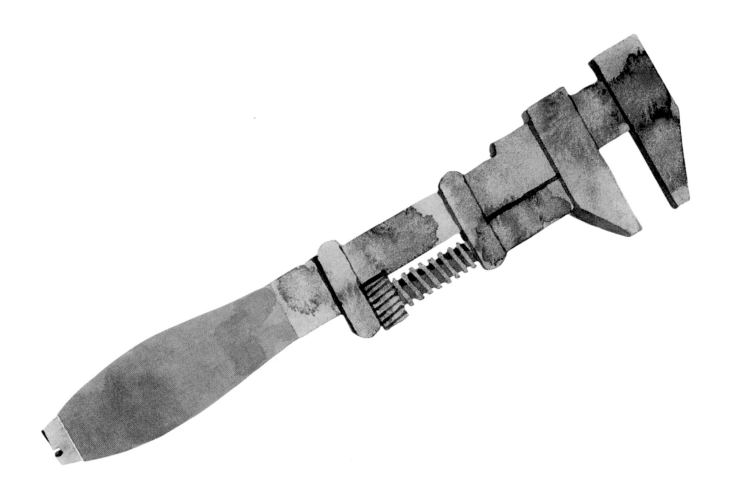

There is a big, strong spanner,

that turns the big, fat nuts
and bolts

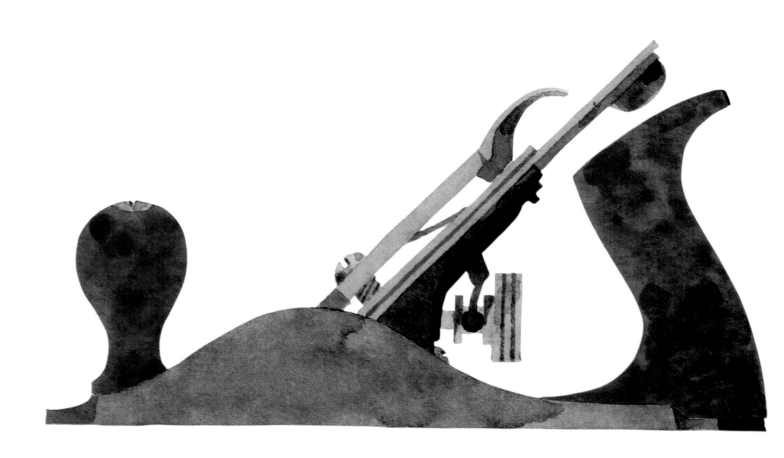

and there is a plane that
smooths wood

and makes curly shavings.

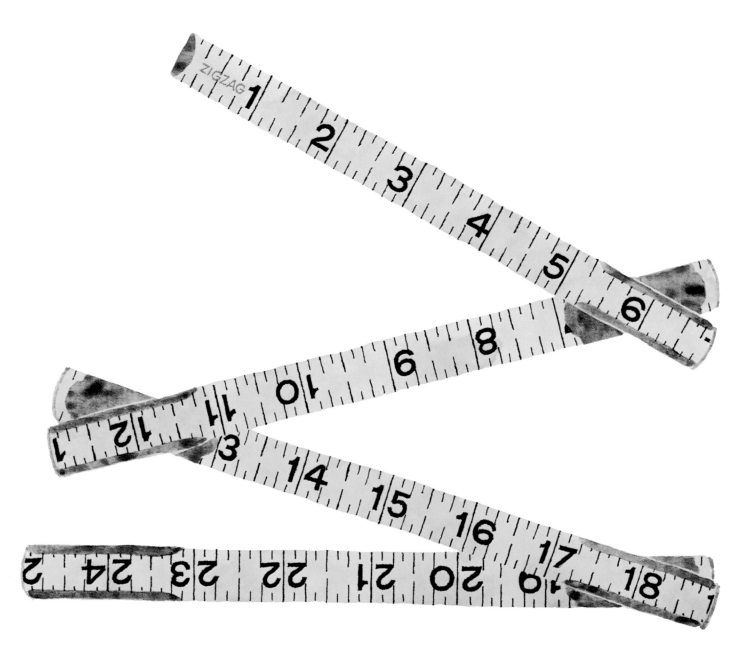

There is a ruler that measures.

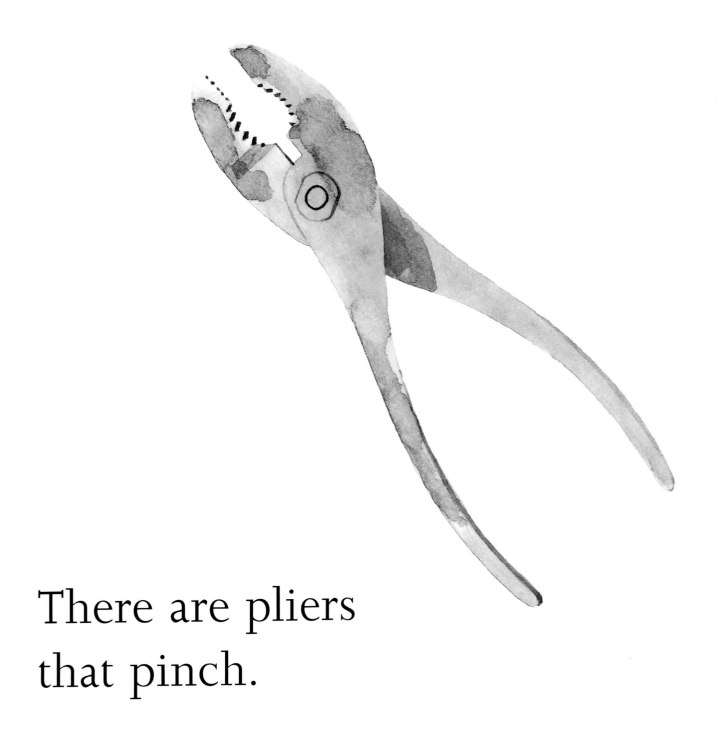

There are pliers
that pinch.

There is sandpaper to smooth
wood and plaster.

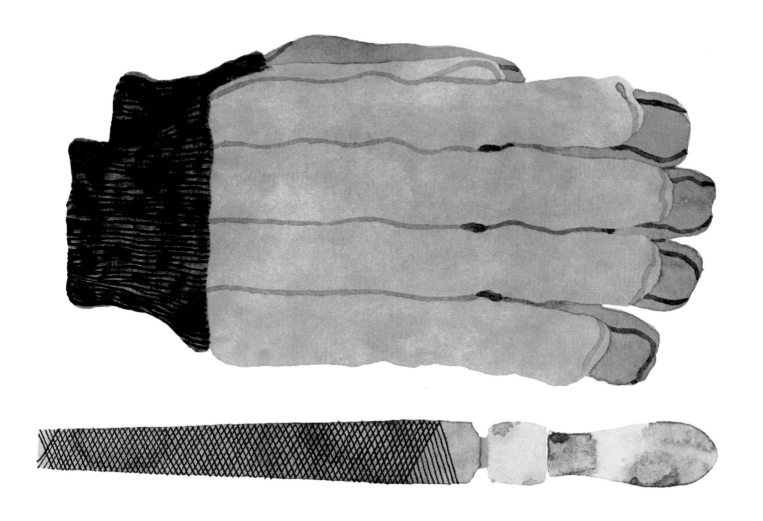

There are work gloves, and there is a file to rub on rough edges of metal to make them smooth.

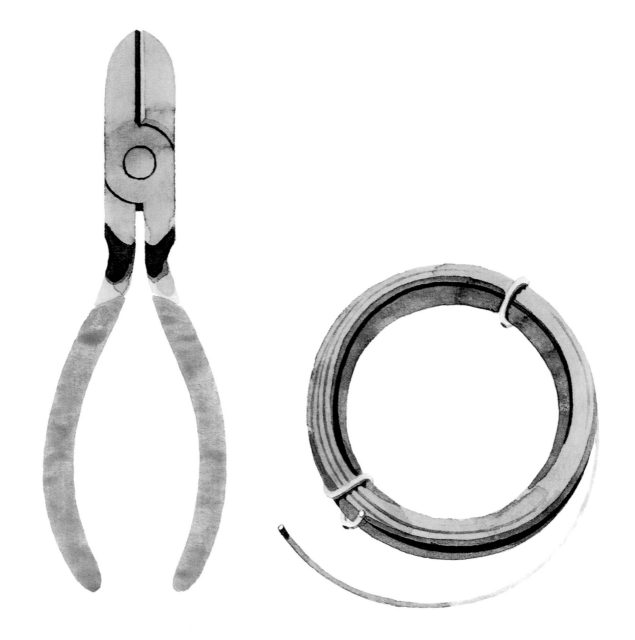

There are sharp wire cutters
and a roll of wire.

There is an oil can with
a tiny hole.

It is my father's toolbox.